BIG AND SMALL

STICKER AND DRAW

closed

open

big

small

short

tall

empty   full

This edition published by Parragon Books Ltd in 2017

Parragon Books Ltd
Chartist House
15–17 Trim Street
Bath BA1 1HA, UK
www.parragon.com

Written by Andrea Turton
Cover illustrated by Olivier Latyk
Illustrated by Beatrice Costamagna, Emma Martinez and Jannie Ho
Edited by Suzi Heal
Designed by Kathryn Davies
Production by Richard Wheeler

ISBN 978-1-4748-6019-2

Printed in China

over

under

Start Little
LEARN BIG

BIG

new

big

AND
SMALL

old

small

STICKER AND DRAW

quiet

loud

PaRRagon

Bath • New York • Cologne • Melbourne • Delhi
Hong Kong • Shenzhen • Singapore

What's the weather like today?

Dress the bears for a hot day and a cold day with your stickers.

sizzle

It's a **hot** day, hooray!

brrrrr

It's a **cold** day, let's play!

Look at the **big** animals!
But where are their **small** ones?

Find a small animal to stick next to each big animal.

Spot and tick these **big** and **small** things.

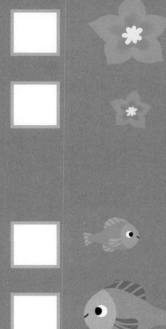

It's lunchtime! Use your food stickers to make the **empty** lunch boxes **full**.

full

empty

full

empty

How do you feel today?
Draw your **happy** face.

What makes you **happy**?

Add tick stickers
if the faces are
happy and cross
stickers if they
are sad.

Draw your **sad** face.

What makes you **sad**?

Phew – riding up the hill is **slow**!

Whee – rolling down the hill is **fast**!

Add more cyclists going **up** and **down** the steep hill.

Harry's hair salon is busy today!
Use your stickers to give everyone the
hairstyles they want – **long** or **short**.

Trace to make these
short things **long**.

The TV is **off**. Use your button sticker to turn it **on**.

OFF

What's on TV today?
Draw a picture!

True or False?

Use your tick stickers to show which are **true**.
Add cross stickers to show which are **false**.

 Dogs go **MOO!**

Cows go **MOO!**

 Tomatoes are **BLUE**.

Tomatoes are **RED**.

Stick to see who is **heavy** and who is **light**.

Look – more **light** things!
Use your stickers to add
the **heavy** things.

Draw something **heavy** here to try to balance the seesaw.

Watch out, it's very wobbly at the **top**!

Draw some eye-catching outfits on the acrobats – use spots and stripes!

It's safer at
the **bottom**!

Spot these
things, then tick
them here!

A pig in
a wig

A rat with
a hat

A cat with
a bat

A fox in
a box

Red Riding Hood is **inside** the house.

Sticker who's **outside** the house.

outside

inside

Rapunzel is **inside** the castle.

Sticker who's **outside** the castle.

inside

outside

over

under

The prince is **over** the sea.

Sticker who's **under** the sea.

The billy goat is **over** the bridge.

Sticker who's **under** the bridge.

over

under

Who lives where? Trace and colour the bird **above** the waves and the fish **below** the waves.

below

above

Sticker who lives **high** up in the sky
and who lives down **low** in the sea.

It's the **lost** and **found** office. Follow the lines to match the lost things to their owners.

The queen has **lost** her crown jewels!
Check your sticker sheet. Have you **found** them?

Uh-oh! Roadworks EVERYWHERE!
Can you help Mr Bear find his way home?

How many green **GO** signs can you see? ☐

How many red **STOP** signs are there? ☐

Welcome to the **Opposites** Shop!
How can we help you today?

Find these opposites in the shop then tick them off your list.

big and **small**

open and **closed**

happy and **sad**

empty and **full**

This little mouse loves to explore.
Find her in the **loud** city and the **quiet** countryside.

It's **loud** in the city!

Colour the cars in bright shades.

beep beep

Stick more **loud** things in the city.

It's **quiet** in the countryside!

Colour the flowers in pretty colours.

tweet tweet

Stick more **quiet** things in the countryside.

The **clean** laundry has been hung out to dry.
But some clothes are still **dirty**!

clean

dirty

Add **clean** clothes to the
washing line with your stickers.

Make this **black** page
look spooky with your
white stickers.

Use your black stickers
to make this **white**
page look freaky.

This is the house of a
very forgetful mouse.

upstairs

downstairs

Help the mouse find these objects in the house. Draw an **UP** or a **down** arrow to show her whether they are **upstairs** or **downstairs**.

Colour these pairs so they all look the **same**.

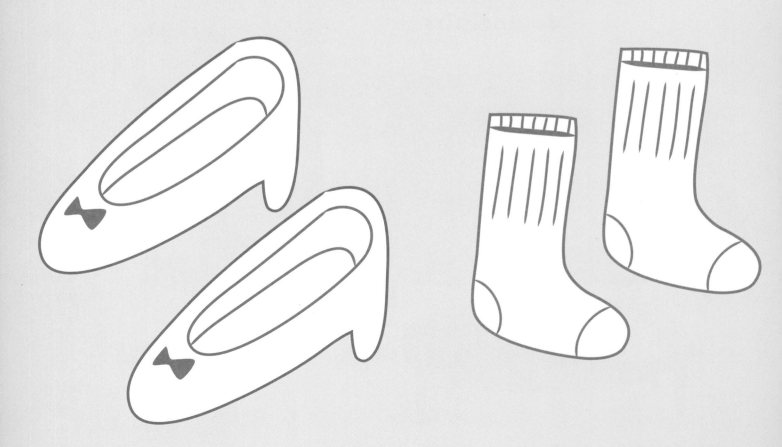

Colour these pairs so they all look **different**.

The alien spaceships need to get home to their planet.

Follow the trails with your finger – which is **straight** and which is **bendy**?

3 spaceships fly **straight** to Earth.
2 spaceships take a **bendy** route.
Draw the trails.

Rise and shine! It's time to wake up!

Add stickers to open everyone's eyes and change them from **asleep** to **awake**.

It's time for bed! But everyone is still wide awake…
Stick to send everyone to sleep.

Yawn!

What time do you go to sleep?

Draw the hands on the clock.

It's **day time**, sunny and bright!

Shhh... it's **night time**, turn on the lights!

Use your **day** and **night**
stickers to finish the pictures.

Can you match all these opposites?

clean

closed

full

dirty

open

smooth

rough

front

back

empty

ON